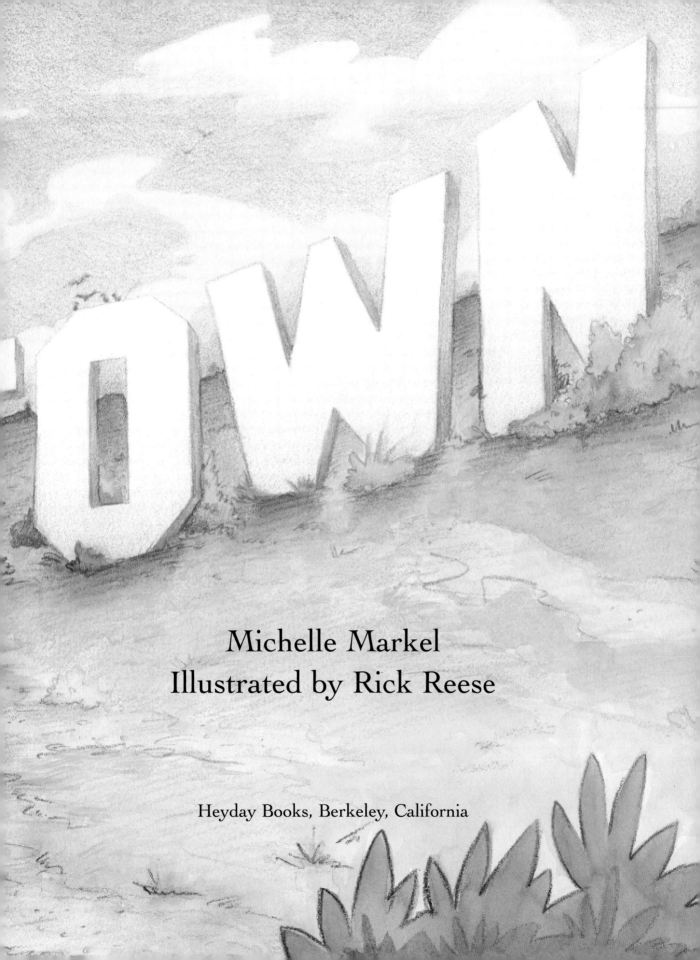

Michelle Markel
Illustrated by Rick Reese

Heyday Books, Berkeley, California

For my sister Carole, who came up with some of the best childhood fantasies of all. And a giant thank you to Cindy Olnick at the Los Angeles Conservancy for her assistance in procuring photos. —Michelle Markel

For Lucy —Rick Reese

Heyday Books, founded in 1974, works to deepen people's understanding and appreciation of the cultural, artistic, historic, and natural resources of California and the American West. It operates under a 501(c)(3) nonprofit educational organization (Heyday Institute) and, in addition to publishing books, sponsors a wide range of programs, outreach, and events.

To help support Heyday or to learn more about us, visit our website at www.heydaybooks.com, or write to us at P.O. Box 9145, Berkeley, CA 94709.

Orders, inquiries, and correspondence should be addressed to:
Heyday Books
P. O. Box 9145, Berkeley, CA 94709
(510) 549-3564, Fax (510) 549-1889
www.heydaybooks.com

Book design by Rebecca LeGates

Printed in China by Phoenix Asia

10 9 8 7 6 5 4 3 2 1

Library of Congress Cataloging-in-Publication Data
Markel, Michelle.
  Dream town / Michelle Markel ; illustrated by Rick Reese.
    p. cm.
  Summary: One snowy day, Nana tells her grandson about the magical town of her childhood, where there were giant dogs and hats, witch houses, and miniature kingdoms of flowers that floated down the street.
  ISBN 1-59714-022-8 (hardcover : alk. paper)
  [1. Los Angeles (Calif.)—Fiction. 2. Grandmothers—Fiction.] I. Reese, Rick, ill. II. Title.
  PZ7.M33945Dre 2006
  [E]—dc22
                                                    2005017855

Credits for the photographs on pages 30–31:
Spadena House courtesy of Bruce Boehner.
Muffler Man courtesy of Mary-Margaret Stratton.
Randy's Donuts courtesy of Lana Cohen.
The Brown Derby [photCL 310(2062)], the Pup Café [photCL 310(2063)], and the Tamale [photCL 310(2066)] reproduced by permission of The Huntington Library, San Marino, California.
Tiny Naylor's Restaurant courtesy of Reibsamen Nickels and Rex; Merge Studios.
The Samson Tire Factory courtesy of the Los Angeles Conservancy.
Capitol Records, the Pan Pacific Auditorium, the Coca-Cola Building, and the LAX Theme Building courtesy of the Los Angeles Public Library.

When my nana told me where she came from, I didn't believe it.
I was slipping on my snow boots to go outside.

"Did you play in the snow when you were a kid?" I asked her.
"We didn't have snow," she said.

"No snow?" I said. "What about fall? Did the leaves turn gold and red?"

"No. Where I came from, sometimes it was cool, sometimes it was warm."

"That sounds boring," I said.

"Boring? I was never bored...

"...I lived in Dream Town."

"There were witches' houses, and castles,

and homes where Aladdin might have lived.

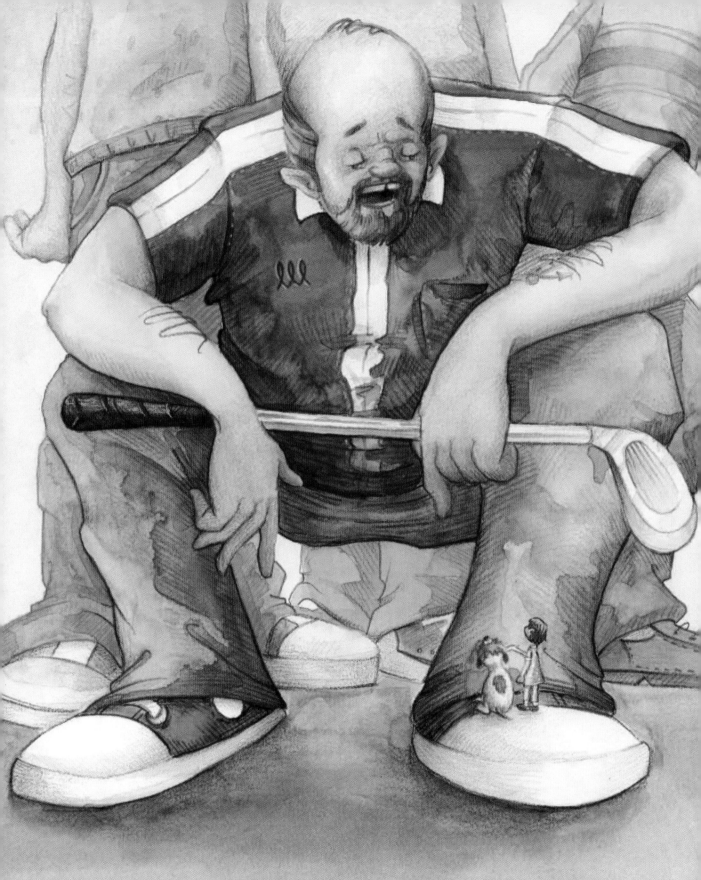

Now and then I'd pay a visit to the giants. There were many.

I knew where to find a giant dog and a humongous hot dog, tamale, and donut for him to eat, a giant hat for him to wear on a warm day, and a giant camera for taking pictures of him.

There was a stack of records
high as the sky,

and tall towers made of seashells, pipes, and pottery.

I could turn the corner and find
an ocean liner,

or a fortress guarded by Assyrian soldiers,

or buildings with fish fins sticking
out of them.

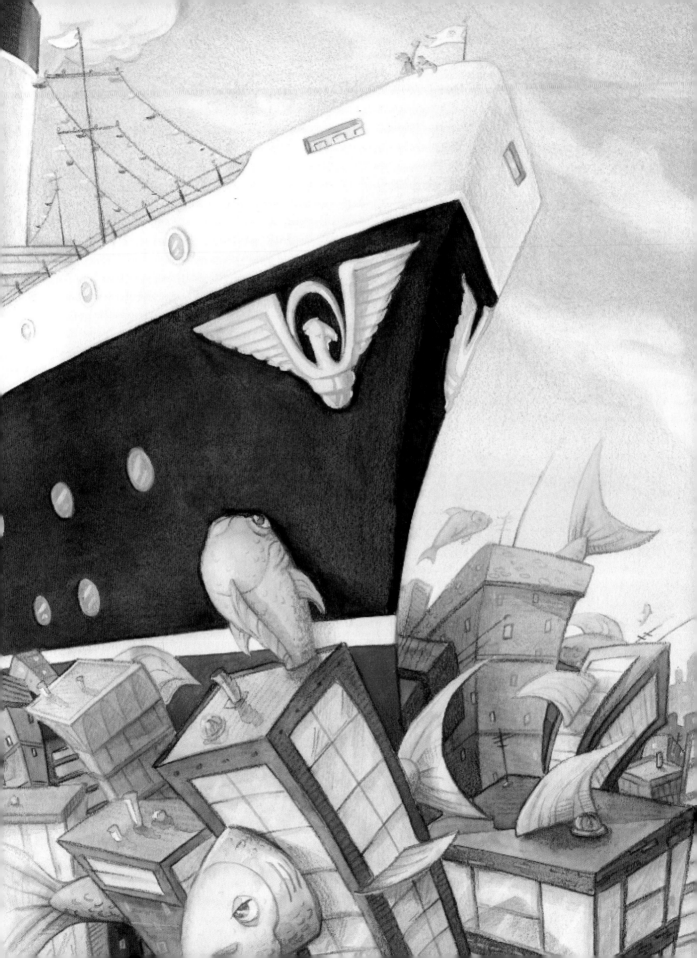

Many times I passed an old Western town

near a glowing space station that served fries and chocolate shakes.

Once a year, I'd smell the flowers of miniature kingdoms
that floated down the street, hear the sizzle and crackle
of stamping dragons,

lose myself in a sea of turtles, snakes,
goats, and parrots.

In the evening, I'd go outdoors and see large
monsters and fairies flickering in the sky.

There were stars everywhere. Night and day
they were in the hills, in the valleys, on the coast,

where the breeze carried the scent of the glittery ocean
and tickled the palm trees before it blew east.

There was so much magic,
I thought there might even be a star inside of me."

"What was the name of this place?" I asked her.

"Los Angeles," she answered.

Then she showed me pictures to prove it!

Spadena House (aka Willat House)
516 Walden Dr., Los Angeles.

Muffler Man
15237 Sherman Way, Van Nuys.

Randy's Donuts,
805 Manchester Blvd., Inglewood.

The Brown Derby
3427 Wilshire Blvd., Los Angeles.

The Pup Cafe
12728 Washington Blvd., Culver City.

The Tamale
6421 Whittier Blvd., Montebello.

Tiny Naylor's Restaurant
NW corner of Sunset and La Brea, Los Angeles.

Samson Tire Factory
5675 Telegraph Rd., City of Commerce.

Capitol Records
1750 Vine St., Los Angeles.

Pan Pacific Auditorium
7600 Beverly Blvd., Los Angeles.

Coca-Cola Building
1334 S. Central Ave., Los Angeles.

LAX Theme Building
209 World Way, Westchester.

Author's Note

In the late 1920s, a strange thing happened on the streets of Los Angeles. Giant animals, huge items of clothing, massive snack foods, and other oddities popped up on the streets. These startling buildings were designed to grab the attention of passing motorists at a time when more and more people were traveling by car. Some buildings, like the Tamale, were in the shape of the food sold inside. Others (the Brown Derby, the Pup Café) looked like the names of the restaurants. Some stores (Randy's Donuts, the Giant) used large sculptures as advertisements. This continued into the 1950s and 1960s.

Also in the 1920s, homes rose up that looked straight out of medieval England (the Spadena house) and other faraway times and places. Theaters, offices, and even the Samson Tire Factory were built to resemble structures from the ancient world. The film industry in Los Angeles, the "dream factory" that created adventure stories set in distant lands, was helping to spread a fever for exotic settings.

A decade later, sleek machines that were really buildings (Coca-Cola, Pan Pacific) showed up in the city. With their streamlined look, rounded corners, and horizontal lines, these structures reminded people of modern trains, ships, and other vehicles. In those days, the speed and efficiency of modern machines promised a solution to the world's problems.

By the 1950s and 1960s, America was exploring outer space. The times were bursting with excitement, and so were the buildings (Tiny Naylor's, the LAX theme building). Roofs jutted into the sky, angles shot into the air, walls glittered, lights beamed like glowing orbs. The circular Capitol Records building is space-age modern (but it also looks like a stack of records!).

Besides its fantastic buildings, L.A. is the home of colorful parades and celebrations, such as the Tournament of Roses, the Golden Dragon Parade, and the Blessing of the Animals.

Many of the buildings referred to in this book are still standing, but several have been torn down. Groups like the Los Angeles Conservancy work hard to save structures like these, which help tell the unique story of Los Angeles. Their website is www.laconservancy.org.